# Sun Kisses, Moon Hugs

By Susan Schaefer Bernardo • Illustrated by Courtenay Fletcher

Inner Flower Child Books
LOS ANGELES

Author **Susan Bernardo** and illustrator **Courtenay Fletcher** are a dynamic duo committed to creating books that heal and inspire children of all ages! Their other books include *The Rhino Who Swallowed a Storm* (co-authored with LeVar Burton) and *The Big Adventures of Tiny House*. Learn more at www.SunKissesMoonHugs.com

Hardcover, 2nd Edition
10 9 8 7 6 5 4 3 2 1
ISBN 978-0-9711228-9-5

Published by
Inner Flower Child Books
17412 Ventura Blvd., Suite 134
Encino, CA 91316

Book design by Courtenay Fletcher
Printed and bound in the United States of America by Bang Printing

Publisher's Cataloging-In-Publication Data (Prepared by The Donohue Group, Inc.)

Names: Bernardo, Susan Schaefer. | Fletcher, Courtenay, illustrator.
Title: Sun kisses, moon hugs / by Susan Schaefer Bernardo; illustrated by Courtenay Fletcher.
Description: Hardcover, 2nd Edition. | Los Angeles : Inner Flower Child Books, 2017. | Interest age level: 002-008.
    | Summary: "In this engaging picture book, children learn that love lasts forever, even when loved ones can't be physically present."--Provided by publisher.
Identifiers: LCCN 2017902436 | ISBN 978-0-9711228-9-5 (hardcover)
Subjects: LCSH: Love--Juvenile fiction. | Families--Juvenile fiction. | Emotions--Juvenile fiction. | Sun--Juvenile fiction. | Moon--Juvenile fiction. | Separation anxiety--Juvenile fiction. | Nature--Juvenile fiction. | CYAC: Love--Fiction. | Families--Fiction. | Emotions--Fiction. | Sun--Fiction. | Moon--Fiction. | Separation anxiety--Fiction. | Nature--Fiction. | LCGFT: Picture books. | Stories in rhyme.
Classification: LCC PZ7.B47 Su 2017 | DDC [E]--dc23

Sealed with a kiss for Mom and Dad
and my sons Brendan and Charlie...
Guess what? You know what? I love you!

_S.B.

For Macallan, who puts rainbows in my heart each day...
and my mom, who taught me to hug the moon.

_C.F.

A million hugs and kisses
to our amazing community of family
and friends, old and new...
your support made this book possible.

xoxo Courtenay and Susan

No matter how far apart we are,
I'll always find ways to tell you I love you.

## How?

From wherever we stand,
you see the moon and I see the moon.

That is how we

can send each other hugs.

Moon hugs?
Yes, moon hugs.

But the moon doesn't have any arms!
It's true the moon cannot reach down to hold your hand,
but she is strong enough to pull waves onto sand.

Her invisible arms rock the tides by night and day,
like my love holds you safely when I am away.

What if the moon is just a sliver?
Still she will deliver an entire quiver full of love.
However small and thin the moon might seem,
the hugs we send always make her beam.

What if there's no moon in sight?
Close your eyes and imagine it bright,
and love will dance in your dreams tonight.

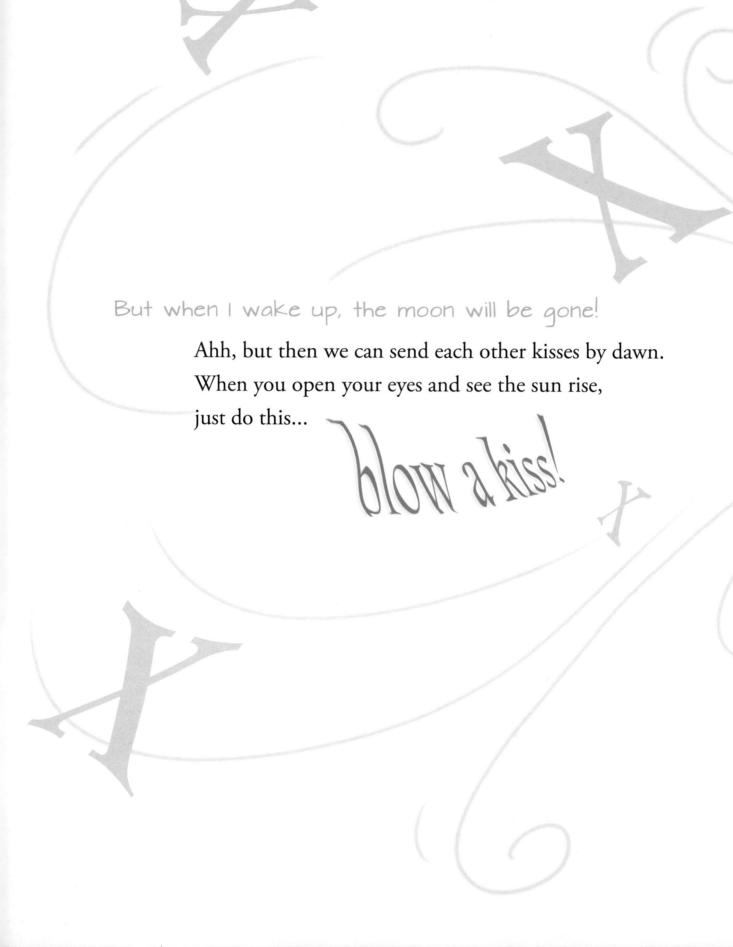

But when I wake up, the moon will be gone!

Ahh, but then we can send each other kisses by dawn.
When you open your eyes and see the sun rise,
just do this...

*blow a kiss!*

The sun will catch your kiss and use light speed to forward it right on to me.

I'll send a million kisses back your way. You'll feel my love in each warm ray.

But what if...

I know what you're about to say...what if the sky is cloudy or gray?

Love travels through raindrops and waters the ground,
flows into rivers and oceans all around.

When the sky clears and the sun joins the show,
our kisses, like wishes, will slide down rainbows.

You know what else is true?

Every ladybug and butterfly,

each dandelion and daisy

that catches your eye or flutters by,

is saying that I'm crazy

about you.

From the heavens above to earth below,
there are infinite ways to say hello.
Love is in each star twinkling in space
and every frosty snowflake tickling your face.

Throw your arms around a tree...I'll hug you and you'll hug me.

Each grain of sand means I'm in reach
when you're playing on the beach.

I'm leaving signs to show I care, like the wind whispering through your hair.

Whenever I miss you,

I will find a way to hug and kiss you.

See these letters X and O?
They're another way for us to show
something forever true...
you love me, and I love you.

Hugs by moon and kisses by sun,
I'll always love you, Little One.